80 003 146 303

KT-417-878

Not a Good Look

by

C. L. Tompsett

Illustrated by Julia Page

Northamptonshire
Libraries

First published in 2008 in Great Britain by
Barrington Stoke Ltd
18 Walker St, Edinburgh, EH3 7LP

www.barringtonstoke.co.uk

Copyright © 2008 C.L. Tompsett
Illustrations © Julia Page

The moral right of the author has been asserted in
accordance with the Copyright, Designs and
Patents Act 1988

Title ISBN: 978-1-84299-624-9
Pack ISBN: 978-1-84299-623-2

Printed in Poland by Pozkal

We ask the author ...

What was your first date like?

My first date was a blind date. I did not know what he would look like or what he would be like. But he looked great and he was good fun to be with. I went out with him for ages!

It was a good day for Kim. She was very happy. Jack had asked her to go out with him.

Jack was the best looking boy in school and all the girls liked him.

"What shall I wear?" Kim asked her best friend Milly.

"Where are you going?" Milly wanted to know.

"Jack didn't say," Kim said. "But I want to look cool."

Kim looked at all her clothes. She didn't see anything she liked.

"I hate all my clothes," she said. "I'll have to buy something new."

Milly said she would go shopping with Kim.

So Saturday morning, they went into town.

Kim looked in all the shops in the Shopping Centre.

She tried on loads of tops.

In the end, she found one she liked.

"My hair is a mess," she said to Milly. "I can't go to the hair-dresser. I've got no money. Will you do my hair for me?"

On Saturday afternoon Milly went to Kim's house.

She did Kim's hair for her.

She made Kim look much older.

"That looks fab!" Kim said. "Will you help me with my make-up too?"

Milly smiled. "I'll even go out with Jack for you, if you like."

"Don't you dare!" Kim said. "He's mine!"

Kim looked in the mirror. Then she saw it.

A spot on the end of her nose! It was a big red spot.

Kim gave a scream. "Look at that! I can't go out with Jack now. He'll think I'm ugly!"

"No, he won't," Milly said.

"I'll hide it with some make-up."

Kim let Milly put some make-up on her nose.

"Now it looks like a big *orange* spot!" Kim said. "I can't let Jack see me like this. I'll have to phone him."

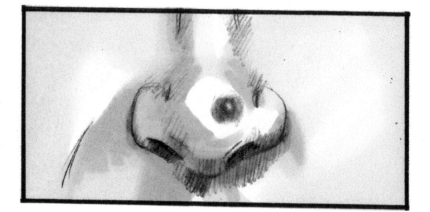

Kim took her mobile out of her bag.

She rang Jack.

"I'm sorry, Jack. I can't go out with you tonight. I'm not well."

Jack asked what was wrong.

Kim said she had a bad cold.

Milly grinned.

"Well in a way that's true," she said. "You have got *something* wrong with your nose."

Kim felt sad.

She had been so happy in the morning.

That was until she'd seen the spot.

Would Jack ever look at her again?

At five o' clock, Milly went home.

Kim took off her make-up and her new top.

She would save it for another day.

She didn't mind if she looked a mess. No one was going to see her.

After tea, she sat down in front of the T.V. Mum was in the kitchen, making a coffee. The door bell rang.

Mum said, "I'll get that."

She went to the door.

Kim stayed where she was.

Mum was talking to someone.

Kim killed the sound on the T.V. so she'd be able to hear who it was.

"Oh, hello, do come in," said Mum. "She's in the living room."

Milly must have come back, Kim said to herself. *Good, we can both watch T.V. now.*

The door opened and Jack walked in.

Kim was shocked.

Jack mustn't see her like this. She had a big red spot on her nose and she looked a mess!

She ran out of the room.

"Kim!" Mum called after her. "Where are you going? Jack's here!"

Kim ran up to her room.

She put on her new top and brushed her hair.

There was no time to do her make-up.

She came back down and went into the living room.

She held a tissue in front of her nose and gave a loud sniff.

It was a warm day but Jack had a scarf on.

It was over his chin.

"I came to see how you were," he said.

"I'm OK," Kim told him.

She kept the tissue over her nose.

"Let me take your scarf," she said.

She took it off Jack's neck. Jack tried to stop her, but it was too late.

There, on his chin, was a big red spot.

Kim grinned at him.

She took the tissue away from her nose.

"SNAP!" she said.